Cheap AND *Easy!*

GE / HOTPOINT WASHER REPAIR

7th EDITION

Written ESPECIALLY for Do-It-Yourselfers, Trade Schools, and other "green" technicians!

By Douglas Emley

Distributed exclusively by:

EB Marketing Group

Lake Havasu City, AZ ● 800-400-3026 ● http://www.appliancerepair.net

General Electric®, GE®, Hotpoint® and RCA® are registered trademarks of the General Electric Company, Schenectady, New York, USA.

Special Thanks to technical consultants Dick Miller, Jose Hernandez,and Woody Randolph, whose collective decades of experience as field appliance service technicians are reflected in the technical information and procedures described in this publication.

Distributed exclusively by:
EB Marketing Group
597 N. Lake Havasu Ave.
Lake Havasu City, AZ 86403
Phone: (800) 400-3026 Fax (800) 400-4419

Printed in the United States of America

HOW TO USE THIS BOOK

STEP 1: READ THE DISCLAIMERS ON THE PREVIOUS PAGE. This book is intended for use by people who have a bit of mechanical experience or aptitude, and just need a little coaching when it comes to appliances. If you don't fit that category, don't use this book! We're all bloomin' lawyers these days, y'know? If you break something or hurt yourself, no one is responsible but **YOU**; not the author, the publisher, the guy or the store who sold you this book, or anyone else. Only **YOU** are responsible, and just by using this book, you're agreeing to that. If you don't understand the disclaimers, get a lawyer to translate them **before** you start working.

Read the safety and repair precautions in section 1-5. These should help you avoid making too many *really* bad mistakes.

STEP 2: READ CHAPTERS 1 & 2: Everything else in this book flows from chapters 1 and 2. If you don't read them, you won't be able to properly diagnose your washer.

Know what kind of washer you have and basically how it works. When you go to the appliance parts dealer, have the nameplate information at hand. Have the proper tools at hand, and know how to use them.

STEP 3: READ CHAPTERS 3 & 4 ABOUT YOUR SPECIFIC MODEL.

STEP 4: FIX THE BLOOMIN' THING! If you can, of course. If you're just too confused, or if the book recommends calling a technician for a complex operation, call one.

WHAT THIS BOOK WILL DO FOR YOU
(and what it won't!)

This book **will** tell you how to fix the most common problems with the most common brands of domestic (household) top-loading washing machines. (This represents 95+ percent of all repairs that the average handyman or service tech will run into.)

This book **will not** tell you how to fix your industrial or commercial or any very large washing machine. The support and control systems for such units are usually very similar in function to those of smaller units, but vastly different in design, service and repair.

We **will** show you the easiest and/or fastest method of diagnosing and repairing your washer.

We **will not necessarily** show you the cheapest way of doing something. Sometimes, when the cost of a part is just a few dollars, we advocate replacing the part rather than rebuilding it. We also sometimes advocate replacement of an inexpensive part, whether it's good or bad, as a simplified method of diagnosis or as a preventive measure.

We **will** use only the simplest of tools; tools that a well-equipped home mechanic is likely to have and to know how to use, including a VOM.

We **will not** advocate your buying several hundred dollars' worth of exotic equipment or special tools, or getting advanced technical training to make a one-time repair. It will usually cost you less to have a professional perform this type of repair. Such repairs represent only a very small percentage of all needed repairs.

We **do not** discuss electrical or mechanical theories. There are already many very well-written textbooks on these subjects and most of them are not likely to be pertinent to the job at hand; fixing your washer!

We **do** discuss rudimentary mechanical systems and simple electrical circuits.

We expect you to be able to look at a part and remove it if the mounting bolts and/or connections are obvious. If the mounting mechanism is complicated or hidden, or there are tricks to removing or installing something, we'll tell you about it.

You are expected to know what certain electrical and mechanical devices are, what they do in general, and how they work. For example, switches, relays, motors, solenoids, cams, clutches, brakes, pullies, idlers, belts, helical shafts, radial and thrust (axial) bearings, flexible motor couplings, splines, water valves, water and oil seals, centrifugal pumps, and pressure diaphragms. If you do not know what these things do, learn them BEFORE you start working on your washer.

You should know how to cut, strip, and splice wire with crimp-on connectors, wire nuts and electrical tape. You should know how to measure voltage and how to test for continuity with a VOM (Volt-Ohm Meter). If you have an ammeter, you should know how and where to measure the current in amps. If you don't know how to use these meters, there's a brief course on how to use them (for *our* purposes *only*) in Chapter 1. See section 1-4 before you buy either or both of these meters.

A given procedure was only included in this book if it passed the following criteria:

1) The job is something that the average couch potato can complete in one afternoon, with no prior knowledge of the machine, with tools a normal home handyman is likely to have.

2) The parts and/or special tools required to complete the job are easily found and not too expensive.

3) The problem is a common one; occuring more frequently than just one out of a hundred machines.

Costly repairs which are included in this book if they pass the following criteria:

1) The cost of the repair is still far less than replacing the machine or calling a professional service technician, and

2) The repair is likely to yield a machine that will operate satisfactorily for several more years, or at least long enough to justify the cost.

In certain parts of the book, the author expresses an opinion as to whether the current value of a particular machine warrants making the repair or "scrapping" the machine. Such opinions are to be construed as opinions ONLY and they are NOT to be construed as legal advice. The decision as to whether to take a particular machine out of service depends on a number of factors that the author cannot possibly know and has no control over; therefore, the responsibility for such a decision rests solely with the person making the decision.

I'm sure that a physicist reading this book could have a lot of fun tearing it apart because of my deliberate avoidance and misuse of technical terms. However, this manual is written to simplify the material and inform the novice, not to appease the scientist.

*NOTE:The diagnosis and repair procedures in this manual do not necessarily apply to brand-new units, newly-installed units or recently relocated units. Although they **may** posess the problems described in this manual, washers that have recently been installed or moved are subject to special considerations not taken into account in this manual for the sake of simplicity. Such special considerations include installation parameters, installation location, the possibility of manufacturing or construction defects, damage in transit, and others.*

This manual was designed to assist the novice technician in the repair of home (domestic) washers that have been operating successfully for an extended period of months or years and have only recently stopped operating properly, with no major change in installation parameters or location.

Table of Contents

CHAPTER 1
WASHER IDENTIFICATION, TOOLS AND SAFETY, TIPS AND TRICKS
1-1 WASHER IDENTIFICATION 1.1
1-2 BEFORE YOU START 1.1
1-3 TOOLS 1.2
1-4 BASIC REPAIR AND SAFETY PRECAUTIONS 1.4
1-5 TIPS & TRICKS 1.5
1-6 HOW TO USE A VOM AND AMMETER 1.6
   1-6(a) TESTING VOLTAGE 1.6
   1-6(b) TESTING FOR CONTINUITY 1.7
   1-6(c) AMMETERS 1.8

CHAPTER 2
PROBLEMS COMMON TO BOTH DESIGNS
2-1 CYCLES 2.1
2-2 FILL SYSTEM 2.3
2-3 PUMP; DRAIN AND RECIRCULATION SYSTEMS 2.7
2-4 LEAKS 2.7
2-5 TRANSMISSION AND DRIVE TRAIN 2.9
   2-5(a) BELTS 2.9
   2-5(b) AGITATOR 2.9
   2-5(c) TRANSMISSIONS 2.10
2-6 TESTING ELECTRICAL COMPONENTS 2.10
2-6(A) SWITCHES AND SOLENOIDS 2.13
   2-6(b) WATER LEVEL SWITCHES 2.14
   2-6(c) TIMERS 2.14
   2-6(d) SPEED SELECTOR AND WATER TEMPERATURE SWITCHES 2.16
   2-6(e) DRIVE MOTORS, START SWITCH, AND CAPACITORS 2.17

CHAPTER 3
OLD-STYLE (PRE-1995) GENERAL ELECTRIC

3-1 BASIC OPERATION 3.1
3-2 OPENING THE CABINET AND CONSOLE 3.2
3-3 WHAT TYPICALLY GOES WRONG WITH THESE MACHINES 3.2
3-4 PUMP AND PUMP COUPLING 3.5
3-5 AGITATOR 3.6
3-6 TUB BOOT SEAL AND TUB FITTINGS 3.7
3-7 TIMER 3.9
3-8 LID SWITCH 3.9
3-9 WATER LEVEL SWITCH 3.9
3-10 BELT 3.10
3-11 CLUTCH 3.10
3-12 MOTOR AND RELAY 3.13
3-13 TRANSMISSION 3.14
3-14 SNUBBER BLOCKS 3.15

CHAPTER 4
GE FRONT-ACCESS (POST-1995) MACHINES

4-1 OPERATING SYSTEM 4.1
4-2 WHAT TYPICALLY GOES WRONG WITH THESE MACHINES 4.2
4-3 CONSOLE 4.4
4-4 CABINET FRONT ACCESS 4.5
4-5 TUB REMOVAL 4.6
4-6 REBUILDING THE LOWER BEARING 4.8

Chapter 1

WASHER IDENTIFICATION TOOLS AND SAFETY TIPS AND TRICKS

1-1 WASHER IDENTIFICATION

Appliance companies, like most other major industries, have their share of takeovers, buyouts and cross-brand agreements.

Some manufacturers "private label" their machines for large department stores. Sears' Kenmore is such an example. Sears does not manufacture appliances. Kenmore washers are, and always have been, private-labelled "Whirlpool" washers, both belt-drive and direct-drive.

GENERAL ELECTRIC: Until 1995, GE had made the same old fairly reliable design for 30 years. These machines were sold as GE, Hotpoint, and "private-labelled" as JC Penney and Penncrest brands.

In 1995, GE started making a new "front access" washing machine. Unlike the old model, there is no rear access panel on these machines; all the machine internals are accessed through the front. These machines were sold as GE, Hotpoint, and RCA machines.

Both the "old-style" and the newer "front-access" GE machine designs are covered in this manual, in chapters 3 and 4.

1-2 BEFORE YOU START

Find yourself a good appliance parts dealer. You can find them in the Yellow Pages under the following headings:

● APPLIANCES, HOUSEHOLD, MAJOR
● APPLIANCES, PARTS AND SUPPLIES
● REFRIGERATORS, DOMESTIC
● APPLIANCES, HOUSEHOLD, REPAIR AND SERVICE

Call a few of them and ask if they are a repair service, or if they sell parts, or both. Ask them if they offer free advice with the parts they sell. (Occasionally, stores that offer parts *and* service will not want to give you advice.) Often, the parts counter men are ex-technicians who got tired of the pressure of going into peoples' houses and selling a job. They can be your best friends; however, you don't want to badger them with TOO many questions, so know your basics before you start asking questions.

Some parts houses may offer service too. Be careful! They may try to talk you out of even *trying* to fix your own washer. They'll tell you it's too complicated, then in the same breath, "guide" you to their service department. Who are you gonna believe, me or them? Not all service/parts places are this way, however. If they genuinely *try* to help you fix it yourself and you find that you can't fix the problem, they may be a really good place to look for service.

When you go into the store, have ready your make, model and serial number from the *nameplate* of the washer.

NAMEPLATE INFORMATION

The metal nameplate information is usually found in one of the places shown in Figure 1-1:

A) Along the bottom panel; on the left or right corner.

B) Inside or underneath the lid.

C) Somewhere on the back of the washer.

D) Side or top of the console

If all else fails, check the original papers that came with your washer when it was new. They should contain the model number SOMEWHERE.

If you have absolutely NO information about the washer anywhere, make sure you bring your old part to the parts store with you. Sometimes they can match an old part by looks or by part number.

1-3 TOOLS (Figure 1-2)

The tools that you may need (depending on the diagnosis) are listed below. Some are optional. The reason for the option is explained.

For certain repairs, you will need a special tool. These are inexpensively available from your appliance parts dealer. They are listed in this book as needed.

SCREWDRIVERS: Both flat and phillips head; two or three different sizes of each. It is best to have at least a stubby, 4" and 6" sizes.

NUTDRIVERS: You will need at least a 1/4" and a 5/16" nut driver. 4" or 6" ones should suffice, but it's better to have stubbies, too.

ELECTRICAL PLIERS or STRIPPERS and DIAGONAL CUTTING PLIERS: For cutting and stripping small electrical wire.

VOM (VOLT-OHM METER): For testing circuits. If you do not have one, get one. An inexpensive one will suffice, as long as it has both "A.C. Voltage" and "Resistance" (i.e. R x 1, R x 10, etc.) settings on the dial. It will do for our purposes. If you are inexperienced in using one, get an analog (pointer) type (as opposed to a digital.)

Figure 1-1 Nameplate Location

ALLIGATOR JUMPERS *(sometimes called a "CHEATER" or "CHEATER WIRE"):* small gauge (14-16 gauge or so) and about 12 to 18 inches long; for testing electrical circuits. Available at your local electronics store. Cost: a few bucks for 4 or 5 of them.

SYRINGE TYPE TURKEY BASTER: For cleaning fill hose and fill solenoid valve strainer screens.

SOCKET WRENCHES

FLASHLIGHT

OPEN END/BOX WRENCHES

BUTT CONNECTORS, CRIMPERS, WIRE NUTS AND ELECTRICAL TAPE: For splicing small wire.

Figure 1-2: Tools

Turkey Baster

Pliers:

Strippers   Diagonals

Screwdrivers: Flat and Phillips Head

Nutdrivers: 1/4" and 5/16"

Open End / Box Wrenches

VOM (Volt-Ohmmeter)

Alligator Jumpers

Socket Wrenches

Flashlight

OPTIONAL TOOLS (Figure 1-3)

SNAP-AROUND AMMETER: For determining if electrical components are energized. Quite useful; but a bit expensive, and there are alternate methods. If you have one, use it; otherwise, don't bother getting one.

CORDLESS POWER SCREWDRIVER OR DRILL/DRIVER WITH MAGNETIC SCREWDRIVER AND NUTDRIVER TIPS: For pulling off panels held in place by many screws. It can save you lots of time and hassle.

Figure 1-3: Optional Tools

Extendable Inspection Mirrors

Clip-On Ammeter

Nutdriver Tip

Flat Tip

Cordless Power Drill-Driver and Tips

Phillips Tip

EXTENDABLE INSPECTION MIRROR: For seeing difficult places beneath the washer and behind panels.

1-4 BASIC REPAIR AND SAFETY PRECAUTIONS

1) Always de-energize (pull the plug or trip the breaker on) any washer that you're disassembling. If you need to re-energize the washer to perform a test, make sure any bare wires or terminals are taped or insulated. Energize the unit only long enough to perform whatever test you're performing, then disconnect the power again.

2) To work underneath the washer sometimes requires leaning the washer back against the wall at a 30- to 45-degree angle. When you do, always block up one corner of the washer as shown in Figure 1-7. NEVER DO THIS ALONE! Always have someone standing by to help you while you work beneath the washer, in case it comes down on you.

3) If the manual advocates replacing the part, REPLACE IT!! You might find, say, a solenoid that has jammed for no apparent reason. Sometimes you can clean it out and lubricate it, and get it going again. The key words here are *apparent reason*. There is a reason that it stopped--you can bet on it--and if you get it going and re-install it, you are running a very high risk that it will stop again. If *that* happens, you will have to start repairing your washer *all* over again. It may only act up when it is hot, or it may be bent slightly...there are a hundred different "what if's." Very few of the parts mentioned in this book will cost you over ten or twenty dollars. Replace the part.

4) If you must lay the washer over on its side, front or back, first make sure that you are not going to break anything off, such as a drain hose or fill valve. Lay an old blanket on the floor to protect the floor and the finish of the washer. And for goodness' sake, make sure you drain the thing completely first!

5) Always replace the green (ground) leads when you remove an electrical component. They're there for a reason. And NEVER EVER remove the third (ground) prong in the main power plug!

6) When opening the washer cabinet or console, remember that the sheet metal parts are have very sharp edges. Wear gloves, and be careful not to cut your hands!

Figure 1-7: Leaning the Washer Against the Wall

To access belts or other parts underneath the washer:

Lean the washer against the wall at a 30 to 45 degree angle and block up the corner with a wood block

CAUTION: ALWAYS HAVE A HELPER STANDING BY IN CASE THE WASHER STARTS TO COME DOWN ON YOU!!!

1-5 TIPS & TRICKS

Following are a few hard-earned pearls of wisdom:

1) When testing for your power supply from a wall outlet, plug in a small appliance such as a shaver or blow dryer. If you're not getting full power out of the outlet, you'll know it right away.

2) If you just can't get that agitator unstuck, your appliance parts dealer has a device called an Agi-Tamer for just such an occurrence. It's basically a heavy-duty rubber balloon that fits under the agitator, and uses water pressure to lift it upwards from underneath.

3) If you need to drain the tub (usually because your pump isn't pumping out) most folks try to bail it out. That's a wet, messy, yucky job, and not very thorough.

Try this instead: use your garden hose as a siphon.

However, when you do, another problem arises: did you ever try to suck a charge of wash water through a fifty-foot garden hose? If you can, you've got one heckuva set of lungs. And what happens when that nice, week-old dirty wash water reaches your mouth?

You guessed it: there's a better way.

What's the point in sucking the water through the hose? To get rid of the air in the hose, right? Well, instead of using *lung suction* to do that, let's use *house pressure*.

Leave your garden hose connected to the faucet, and put the other end of it in the washer tub. Turn the faucet on for a few seconds, until it stops bubbling in the tub. The air is gone now, right?

Kink the garden hose so you don't lose the water charge, and disconnect it from the faucet. When you're sure the faucet end of the hose is lower than the bottom of the washer tub, release the kink in the hose. The tub will drain, almost completely, in just a few minutes. No muss, no fuss.

1-6 HOW TO USE A VOM AND AMMETER

Many home handymen are very intimidated by electricity. It's true that diagnosing and repairing electrical circuits requires a *bit* more care than most operations, due to the danger of getting shocked. But there is no mystery or voodoo about the things we'll be doing. Remember the rule in section 1-4 (1); while you are working on a circuit, energize the circuit only long enough to perform whatever test you're performing, then take the power back off it to perform the repair. You need not be concerned with any theory, like what an ohm is, or what a volt is. You will only need to be able to set the VOM onto the right scale, touch the test leads to the right place and read the meter.

In using the VOM (Volt-Ohm Meter) for our purposes, the two test leads are always plugged into the "+" and "-" holes on the VOM. (Some VOMs have more than two holes.)

1-6(a) TESTING VOLTAGE (Figure 1-4)

Set the dial of the VOM on the lowest VAC scale (A.C. Voltage) over 120 volts. For example, if there's a 50 setting and a 250 setting on the VAC dial, use the 250 scale, because 250 is the lowest setting over 120 volts.

Touch the two test leads to the

Figure 1-4: Testing Voltage

Set VOM on the proper A.C. Voltage scale

Correct reading is 110 to 125 Volts

Do not jam or force test leads into wall outlet

Standard Wall Outlet

Component being tested for voltage (in this case, a solenoid)

Solenoid Leads

Touch Test leads to Metal Contacts (i.e. terminals or bare wire ends) metal contacts of a live power source, like a wall outlet or the terminals of the motor that you're testing for voltage. (*Do not* **jam** *the test leads into a wall outlet!*) If you are getting power through the VOM, the meter will jump up and steady on a reading. You *may* have to convert the scale in your head. For example, if you're using the 250 volt dial setting and the meter has a "25" scale, simply divide by 10; 120 volts would be "12" on the meter.

1-6(b) TESTING FOR CONTINUITY (Figure 1-5)

Don't let the word "continuity" scare you. It's derived from the word "continuous." In an electrical circuit, electricity has to flow *from* a power source back *to* that power source. If there is any break in the circuit, it is not continuous, and it has no continuity.

"Good" continuity means that there is no break in the circuit.

For example, if you were testing a solenoid to see if it was burned out, you would try putting a small amount of power through the solenoid. If it was burned out, there would be a break in the circuit, the electricity wouldn't flow, and your meter would show no continuity.

That is what the resistance part of your VOM does; it provides a small electrical current (using batteries within the VOM) and measures how fast the current is flowing. For our purposes, it doesn't matter how *fast* the current is flowing; only that there *is* current flow.

To use your VOM to test continuity, set the dial on (resistance) R x 1, or whatever the lowest setting is. Touch the metal parts of the test leads together and read the meter. It should peg the meter all the way on the right side of the

Figure 1-5: Testing Continuity

No need to remove the component from the dishwasher. Just disconnect power and isolate the component electrically. First, set the meter to the lowest resistance scale; (usually R X 1.)

Then touch the test leads together and zero the meter using the thumbwheel.

Then touch test leads to metal or bare wire ends.

Good Continuity: meter needle moves towards right side of scale.

Bad Continuity: meter needle stays towards left side of scale.

scale, towards "0" on the meter's "resistance" scale. If the meter does not read zero resistance, adjust the thumbwheel on the front of the VOM until it *does* read zero. If you cannot get the meter to read zero, the battery in the VOM is low; replace it.

If you are testing, say, a solenoid, first make sure that the solenoid leads are not connected to anything, especially a power source. If the solenoid's leads are still connected to something, you may get a reading through that something. If there is still live power on the item you're testing for continuity, you will burn out your VOM instantly and possibly shock yourself.

Touch the two test leads to the two bare wire ends or terminals of the solenoid. You can touch the ends of the wires and test leads with your hands if necessary to get better contact. The voltage that the VOM batteries put out is very low, and you will not be shocked. If there is NO continuity, the meter won't move. If there is GOOD

continuity, the meter will move toward the right side of the scale and steady on a reading. This is the resistance reading and it doesn't concern us; we only care that we show good continuity. If the meter moves only very little and stays towards the left side of the scale, that's BAD continuity; the solenoid is no good.

If you are testing a switch, you will show little or no resistance (good continuity) when the switch is closed, and NO continuity when the switch is open. If you do not, the switch is bad.

1-6(c) AMMETERS

Ammeters are a little bit more complex to explain without going into a lot of electrical theory. If you own an ammeter, you probably already know how to use it.

If you don't, don't get one. Ammeters are expensive. And for *our* purposes, there are other ways to determine what an ammeter tests for. If you don't own one, skip this section.

Figure 1-6: Testing Amperage

No need to remove the component from the washer

Connected to a power source.

Clip ammeter around one lead only.

No continuity: component not operating. Break somewhere in circuit. Drawing zero amps.

Set ammeter to an appropriate scale, say 0-10 or 0-20 amps

Connected to a power source.

Good continuity: Component operating. Drawing significant amps.

For our purposes, ammeters are simply a way of testing for continuity without having to cut into the system or to disconnect power from whatever it is we're testing.

Ammeters measure the current in amps flowing through a wire. The greater the current that's flowing *through* a wire, the greater the density of the magnetic field it produces *around* the wire. The ammeter simply measures the strength of this magnetic field, and thus the amount of current, flowing through the wire. To determine continuity, for our purposes, we can simply isolate the component that we're testing (so we do not accidentally measure the current going through any other components) and see if there's *any* current flow.

To use your ammeter, first make sure that it's on an appropriate scale (0 to 10 or 20 amps will do). Isolate a wire leading directly to the component you're testing. Put the ammeter loop around that wire and read the meter. (Figure 1-6)

Chapter 2
PROBLEMS COMMON TO BOTH DESIGNS

Washing machine designs vary widely, but there are *some* things that *all* washers have in common. For example, all washers have an electric motor. All washers have both spin and agitate cycles. And since both cycles are driven by the same electric motor, all washers have some sort of mechanism to change between the two.

All washers must also have a way of filling the tub with wash water and a way of draining out used wash water.

And incidental to this, all washers must have a way of controlling water level in the tub, to prevent spillage by overfill or by centrifugal force during the spin cycle.

All washers must (by law) have a mechanism that brakes the spinning basket at the end of the spin cycle, or else a lid lock to prevent the lid from being opened during or shortly after the spin cycle.

And last but not least, all washers must have a timer that controls and coordinates the start, stop and duration of the various cycles.

2-1 CYCLES

FILL CYCLE

During the FILL cycle, a solenoid-operated water mixing valve opens and allows hot or cold water (or both) to enter the tub. There is no pump operating at this time; the tub fills strictly from house pressure. Similarly, there is no heater in your washer; the heat comes from the water heater in your home.

When the water in the tub reaches a certain level, a pressure switch closes the water solenoid valve(s).

Figure G-1: Typical Drive Train

- Tub
- Basket
- Spline
- Water Level
- Driveshaft
- Agitator
- Spin Tube is connected to the basket
- Agitator Shaft
- Transmission
- Pump
- Belt
- Clutch
- Motor

WASH/RINSE (AGITATION) CYCLE

After the water valve closes, an electric motor starts which drives the transmission, through a beltand a clutch. The transmission converts the rotary motion of the motor to the back-and-forth motion of the agitator. A driveshaft extends from the top of the transmission to the agitator, where it is connected to the agitator, usually by a spline. (See Figure G-1.)

Agitation will continue for a certain amount of time, which is controlled by the timer. During agitation, some washers use their pump to circulate water, sucking it from the bottom of the tub and pumping it to the top of the tub. The pump is driven by the same electric motor.

Also during the agitation cycle, bleach or softener may be automatically added. This is usually done by a solenoid valve that allows some of the recirculated water to flush out the bleach or softener dispenser. In some models there is no water circulation involved; the solenoid simply opens a valve or door that lets the dispenser contents drop into the wash water. The timer tells this solenoid valve when to open.

SPIN AND DRAIN CYCLES

After agitation comes a drain cycle, sometimes combined with a spin cycle. During the drain cycle, the pump sucks water from the tub and sends it down the drain. During the spin cycle, the same motor that drove the agitator now drives a spin tube which is concentric with the agitator shaft. (See Figure G-1) The spin tube spins the basket, slinging excess water out of the clothes by centrifugal force. There is a clutch arrangement which allows the basket to come up to speed slowly. This prevents a heavy load from being thrown onto the motor suddenly. It also allows a "pre-pump" action; the water has a chance to drain out of the tub before the basket gets up to speed, preventing the water from overflowing the edge of the tub by centrifugal force.

Some machines have a partial drain cycle only, then refill and agitate again. Some start spinning and draining at the same time. Some only drain until the water reaches a certain level, then start spinning. GE washers have lid switches that stop the basket from spinning when the lid is open.

At the end of the spin cycle, or whenever the lid is lifted, most models have a braking arrangement that stops the tub from spinning. This helps to pre-

Figure G-2: Typical Fill Solenoid Valve

Solenoid Terminals

Water Outlet

Hot and Cold Water Inlets

vent people from accidently sticking their hands into a spinning basket.

CAUTION: NEVER BYPASS THE LID SWITCH, EXCEPT FOR TEST PURPOSES. IF IT IS DEFECTIVE, INSTALL A NEW ONE. THEY ARE THERE FOR A REASON. NO JOKE: I PERSONALLY HAVE A NEPHEW WHOSE ARM WAS TORN OFF (AT 2 YEARS OLD) BECAUSE OF A BYPASSED LID SWITCH!

2-2 FILL SYSTEM

The basic components of the fill system are the hoses, the fill valve, and the pressure or float switch.

The fill valve (Figure G-2) is simply a solenoid valve that opens when activated and allows hot and/or cold water to flow into the tub. Most modern washers use dual solenoid valves, which have both hot and cold solenoids in one valve body. When *warm* water is desired, both valves open to mix hot and cold.

In the newest digital washers, water temperature may be controlled by a "thermistor." A thermistor is a variable resistor; a resistor whose resistance varies according to what temperature it senses. The thermistor's signal goes to the washer's control board (computer,) which opens or closes hot and cold water valves to control the incoming water temperature.

When the water in the tub reaches the desired level, the pressure or float switch closes the circuit to the fill valve. Float switches are pretty rare; you'll find them only in older washers. A diaphragm-type pressure switch is more common. Typical float and pressure switches are shown in Figure G-3. A few old washers used a pressure switch mounted on the BOTTOM of the tub; these are known as water weight switches. They are rare.

DIAGNOSIS

If your washer is not filling properly, or is overflowing, there could be several reasons.

Figure G-3: Typical Water Level Switches

Typical Diaphragm Pressure Switch

Pressure Tube

Float

Typical Float Switch

Tub

SLOW OR NO FILL, OR WATER TOO HOT OR TOO COLD

If your washer is filling very slowly or not at all, or the water temperature is always too hot or too cold, check the fill hose and valve strainers. These are little screens placed in the fill hose and/or water valve to prevent rust and scale from your house's piping system from getting into the water valve. The strainers can get clogged up over time and prevent water flow.

Shut off the water valves and remove the hoses. Look into the both ends of each hose and into the water valve mounted on the washer. In at least one of the three places you should see a strainer screen. (Figure G-4) If it is clogged, you can try cleaning it out with a toothbrush and/or a turkey baster. If you cannot clean the screen sufficiently, you may need to

Figure G-4: Fill Strainer Screens

Flush Strainer Screen with Turkey Baster

Use Pan To Catch Runoff

Screen Sometimes in Hose End

Strainer Screens

replace it. In some instances, the screen is non-removable, and you will need to replace the hose or valve. Neither is very expensive.

When re-installing the hoses, always use new hose washers. Also, take care

Figure G-5: Checking Voltage Across Water Solenoid Valve Coils

Touch test leads to the live solenoid leads

WARNING: LEADS ARE LIVE! DO NOT SHOCK YOURSELF!

Solenoid Leads

For safety, or if the solenoid valve is in a tight spot, you can take power off the machine and use your alligator jumpers to connect the test leads to the solenoid leads. Then power up the machine and read your voltage on the meter.

not to overtighten the hose on the plastic threads of the solenoid valve; tighten just enough to stop it from leaking. If there is any question about the watertight integrity of the hose, replace it. A hose costs a lot less than a new floor or carpeting, which is what you'll be buying if it breaks while you're not home.

If the strainers look O.K., set your temperature control to "warm" and set your timer in the fill cycle. Raise the lid of the washer and depress any lid switch with a pen or screwdriver. Feel the water entering the washer. If it is too hot or too cold, or if no water is coming out at all, test for voltage across each solenoid coil of the water valve as shown in figure G-5. It should read 110 to 125 volts.

If so, you're getting power to your valve, but it's not opening. Replace the valve.

If you're not getting power to the valve, refer to the wiring diagram for your machine (see section 2-6) and trace the source of the interruption. Sometimes it's a broken wire, but more commonly, there will be a problem with the water level switch, timer, lid switch, or temperature switch. Replace the defective switch.

If your washer is a late-model digital machine with a fill thermistor, a defective thermistor might be sending the wrong signal to the control board. Replacing the thermistor (they're not too expensive) will usually solve the problem. The control board may also be defective.

CAUTION: On some brands, you must raise the top of the cabinet to get to the solenoid valve. If your washer has a mercury-tube type lid switch, raising the top of the cabinet may have the same effect on the lid switch as raising the lid. Your washer may not fill or cycle. You will need to jumper the mercury switch to perform any tests when the cabinet top is raised.

OVERFILL

As the tub fills, water pressure increases at the bottom of the tub. This pressure is transmitted to the diaphragm in the water level switch by a rubber or plastic tube. (Figure G-6) When the tub reaches the right level, the diaphragm trips the switch, closing the solenoid fill valve and starting the agitate cycle.

If the tube or diaphragm is leaking badly, the water level switch will not sense any pressure, and thus will not shut off the water flow, so the tub will overflow. If this tube is leaking *slowly*, the washer may exhibit odd fill symptoms. For example, depending

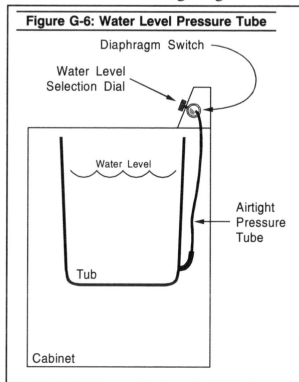

Figure G-6: Water Level Pressure Tube

Diaphragm Switch

Water Level Selection Dial

Water Level

Airtight Pressure Tube

Tub

Cabinet

on how fast the air leak is, the washer may fill and start agitating, then stop agitating and fill some more, then agitate some more, and so forth, until the washer overfills.

CAUTION: Whenever you remove the tube from the switch, or insert the tube onto the switch, there cannot be any water in the tub or tube. Before you insert the tube onto the switch, blow into the tube first, to clear it of any water that might have gotten in it. ANY WATER REMAINING IN THE TUBE WILL CAUSE YOUR WASHER TO OVERFILL, OR PROBABLY EVEN TO OVERFLOW!

Also test the water level switch electrically, as described in section 2-6(b).

DOES NOT STOP FILLING, AND/OR WATER LEVEL KEEPS GOING DOWN

If the house washer drain starts backing up, you get a rooter and clear the drain, right? But *some* people would just seal it up so it couldn't overflow, instead of clearing the drain, as they should. (Now, *WE* wouldn't do that, would we, folks?)

But that air break between the washer's drain hose and the house's drain pipe is important. If there is no air break, and the drain system fills with water, it can actually start siphoning water right through the pump and down the drain. Depending on how bad the drain is backing up, the washer might never fill completely; the solenoid valve will just stay open and water will just keep siphoning straight out the drain. Or, if the drain is a little more clogged and the water is flowing more slowly, the washer might fill and start agitating, but stop agitating after a few minutes and fill some more. This fill-agitate-fill-agitate cycle will continue for as long as the agitate cycle lasts. And since the power to the timer motor is being interrupted, the wash and rinse cycles may seem unusually long.

There is a solution, even if you don't want to root out the drain blockage as you should. Your appliance parts dealer has a drain line vacuum break valve, available for just a few bucks. (Figure G-7) You can cut into your drain line and install one of these vacuum breaks pretty easily.

When the drain line is under pressure, (like when the pump is pumping out) the flapper valve closes and no leakage occurs. When the drain line is under a vacuum (like when the drain is trying to siphon it) the flapper valve opens and air is allowed into the drain line, breaking the siphoning action.

Figure G-7: Vacuum Break Valve

Pump Pressure Closes Valve

Water Out to Drain

Pump Pressure

Air

Vacuum Opens Valve and Lets Air into Drain Hose To Break Vacuum and Prevent Siphoning Action

Vacuum

Siphoning Action

2-3 PUMP; DRAIN AND RECIRCULATION SYSTEMS

The pump can perform several functions. In all washers, it is used to pump water out of the tub at the end of an agitate or soak cycle. In some washers, it also circulates water during the agitate cycle. It may also provide flush water for a bleach or softener dispenser. Therefore, the pump *may* be required to pump in two different directions or more during a cycle.

Older GE washers accomplish this by using two different pump impellers in one body; the pump body has two inlets and two outlets.

New-style GE machines have a separate drain pump with its own separate drive motor. There is no recirculating pump attached to the main drive motor.

DIAGNOSIS

Sometimes the most obvious answers are the first ones overlooked. If the tub isn't draining, first check the drain system. Check the drain hose to make sure it isn't kinked. Also check any lint filter that may be installed.

There aren't too many things that can go wrong with a pump. The pump bearings can seize, stopping it from turning. The pump can be jammed by socks or other small items. The impeller blades can break off due to junk entering the pump; if this happens, the pump may seize up, or it may just stop pumping. The usual solution is to replace the pump.

But the *symptoms* of a pump failure are something else altogether. If the pump locks up, and the motor is still trying to turn it, *something's* gotta give. In old-style GE washers, the pump cou-

pling will be twisted and the motor should trip out on the overload.

*NOTE: If you **EVER** find a broken belt, check for a locked transmission before replacing the belt.*

If you suspect that something is jamming the pump, drain the tub and pull the hoses off the pump. Look into the hoses and the pump and pull out whatever is jamming it. If you can't see anything jamming the pump, feel around the inside of the pump inlets and outlets with a pair of needlenose pliers. If all else fails, and you still can't find the jam, pull the pump out of the machine and check it.

For specific information about pump replacement or service, see the chapter about *your* model.

2-4 LEAKS

Although there are a few leaks common to all brands, most brands have leaks that are peculiar to their design. GE, Whirlpool, Maytag, and others all have common and well-known leak areas. After reading this section, see the chapter about specific models for details.

A common "leak" zone is not a leak at all; the wall drain backs up and overflows onto the floor. This is commonly misdiagnosed as a leak. It can be difficult to diagnose; the problem may be intermittent. Depending on how badly the drain is clogged, there may be a little water or a lot, or it may only overflow every second or third load. While diagnosing a leak, do not be too quick to write this diagnosis off.

If you suspect that your drain is backing up, but you can't quite ever be there at the right time to *observe* the overflow, try this: wrap some toilet paper around the drain hose just above the wall drain pipe. If it backs up, the paper will get wet. Even if you're not there when it happens and the paper dries out, it will have crinkled up, and you'll know your drain's backing up.

If it isn't the drain, run the machine with a full load. Without moving the machine, get right down on the floor and look under the machine with a flashlight. Try to find the general area where water is dripping to the floor; front or back of the machine, left or right side.

Open the cabinet and look for mineral or soap deposits where there shouldn't be any. Trace the deposits in the natural direction of waterflow (against gravity or centrifugal force) back to the source of the leak. Fill the machine again and run it through a cycle or two. Be patient; use your eyes and your brains. There is no magic, easy way to detect a leak.

The *usual* places are:

WATER VALVE: The guts of the fill solenoid valve sometimes will corrode. You may see water leaking from, or rust on the top of the solenoid. (See figure G-7A) Since the valves only open during a fill cycle, this may appear as an intermittent leak. The solution is to replace the valve.

PUMP: Usually from around the pulley seal. Some washer pumps have a hole that allows water to weep out when the seal starts to go bad. The solution is to replace or rebuild the pump.

BLEACH DISPENSERS: Bleach is *VERY* hard on plastic parts. If the bleach dispenser gets old and brittle, it can crack or break off, and the flush water can leak out. But since the dispenser may only be flushed at certain times in the cycle, this will appear as an intermittent leak. The solution is to replace the dispenser, or if you don't use it any more, plug the hose and seal the cracked dispenser with RTV (silicone seal.)

HOSES: Though hose leaks are a bit less common than other leaks, any hoses with a few too many miles on them may be suspect. Replace the hose.

TUB: If the tub is rotted through, it's probably time to replace the washer. If a consistent imbalance in the basket has caused it to wear a hole in the tub (not an uncommon experience to old-style GE washers) then you *may* be able to fix it with an epoxy patch. Ask your appliance parts dealer for an epoxy patch kit.

Figure G-7A: Leaky Water Solenoid Valve

Look for rust or mineral deposits on top of solenoid coils

2-5 TRANSMISSION AND DRIVE TRAIN

Besides driving the pump in old-style GE washers, the main drive motor has two main functions: to spin the basket and reciprocate the agitator. One motor is used to do both.

The spin motion comes directly from the rotary motion of the motor, through the clutch.

There must also be some mechanism to change between spin and agitate. GE machines use a direct-reversing motor to do this. When the motor turns one way, a mechanical arrangement within the transmission engages and the whole transmission spins. Since the top of the transmission is attached to the beaket, the basket spins. When the motor reverses, the brake locks the basket and the transmission internals engage, so the agitator agitates.

2-5(a) BELTS

Look closely at the surface of the belt. If you see any of the problems shown in figure G-8, replace it.

Broken or worn out belts are a common problem. See the chapter on *your* brand for specific details about changing the belt(s) on your model. If you **EVER** find a broken belt, check for a locked pump, transmission or other pulley before replacing the belt.

2-5(b) AGITATOR

If your washer is agitating weakly or not at all, the splines that connect it to the driveshaft may be stripped. It's a fairly common problem. Old-style machines have a rubber spline bushing inside the agitator that can be repplaced. Remove the agitator as described in the chapter specific to your model. If the shaft *is* rotating but the agitator is *not*, replace the agitator or spline insert.

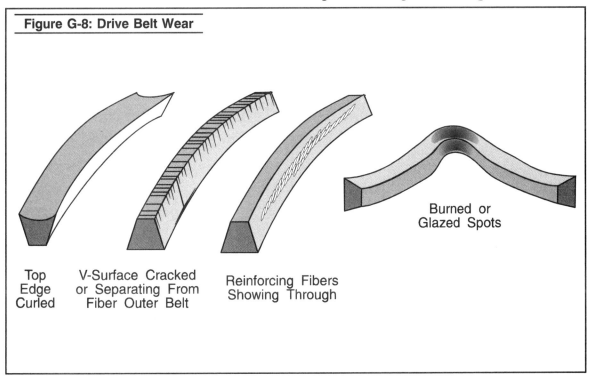

Figure G-8: Drive Belt Wear

Top Edge Curled

V-Surface Cracked or Separating From Fiber Outer Belt

Reinforcing Fibers Showing Through

Burned or Glazed Spots

2-5(c) TRANSMISSIONS

Transmissions in general are pretty bullet-proof, and rarely experience problems beyond a little oil loss. There are exceptions; see the chapter pertaining to your washer.

If your transmission is leaking oil badly, you basically have two options: replace the transmission now, or keep running it until it runs out of oil and dies. Nobody I know of rebuilds transmissions themselves any more. It is far quicker and easier to just replace it with a rebuilt. See the chapter about your model for replacement details.

Occasionally, something will break inside the casing and lock the transmission, or prohibit its operation in one mode or another.

The symptoms may be similar to a locked pump; stalled motor, burning belt, etc. Since the transmission is driven through the clutch in GE machines, you may also smell the clutch burning.

To diagnose this, first unplug your washer. Try turning the motor by hand, or pull the belt so everything rotates. *Be careful you don't pinch your fingers between the belt and pulley!* Check to see that every pulley that the belt rides is rotating. It should be pretty stiff, but if you can't turn it at all, something is locked up. Disengage the drive system (remove the belt, etc.) Try to turn the transmission drive pulley with your hand. Also check the movement of the pump, and any tensioner or idler pulley that may be present.

Do not try to rebuild your own transmission. Typically, rebuilding requires special tools that drive the cost above that of buying a rebuilt transmission. Rebuilt trannies for the more popular models are inexpensively available from your parts dealer, and usually kept in stock.

There are a few very poor designs out there that are not worth fixing; you are better off scrapping the washer. Due to some parts business politics, I can't mention brand names in this book, but your parts dealer will probably be happy to privately let you know which ones they are.

2-6 TESTING ELECTRICAL COMPONENTS

Sometimes you need to read a wiring diagram, to make sure you are not forgetting to check something. Sometimes you just need to find out what color wire to look for to test a component. It is ESPECIALLY important in diagnosing a bad timer.

If you already know how to read a wiring diagram, you can skip this section. If you're one of those folks who's a bit timid around electricity, all I can say is read on, and don't be too nervous. It will come to you. You learned how to use a VOM in Chapter 1, right?

Look at figure G-9. The symbol used to represent each component is pretty universal, and each component should be labelled clearly on your diagram.

A few notes about reading a wiring diagram:

Notice that in some parts of the diagram, the lines are thicker than in other parts. The wiring and switches that are shown as thick lines are *inside* of the timer.

The small circles all over the diagram are terminals. These are places where you can disconnect the wire from the component for testing purposes.

If you see dotted or shaded lines around a group of wires, this is a switch assembly; for example, a water level, water temperature or motor speed switch assembly. It may also be the timer, but whatever it is, it should be clearly marked on the diagram. Any wiring enclosed by a shaded or dotted box is internal to a switch assembly and must be tested as described in sections 2-6(c) and 2-6(d).

Switches may be numbered on the diagram, but that number will *not* be found on the switch. Those numbers are there to help you follow the timer sequencing chart. Don't worry about the timer sequencing chart. We are only concerned to see *if* the switch is opening and closing. We'll let the design engineers worry about exactly *when* it opens and closes.

To find (and test) a switch with a certain number, look for the color of the wires leading to the switch.

Wire colors are abbreviated; for example, BU means blue, BL or B means black, V means violet, T means tan. If you see a wire color with a dash or a slash, that means —— with a —— stripe. For example, OR-W means orange with a white stripe; G/P means green with a pink stripe.

NOTE: *Green wires are ground wires and MUST be re-connected when removed.*

Remember that for something to be energized, it must make a complete electrical circuit. You must be able to trace the path that the electricity will take, FROM the wall outlet back TO the wall outlet. This includes not only the component that you suspect, but all switches leading to it. In Figure G-9(a), L1 and L2 are the main power leads; they go directly to your wall plug.

Let's say you need to check out why the spin solenoid is not working. Following the gray-shaded circuit in figure G-9(a), the electricity flows through the black wire (L1) to the push-pull switch. This switch is located inside of the timer (you know this because it is drawn with thick lines) and it must be closed. The power then goes through

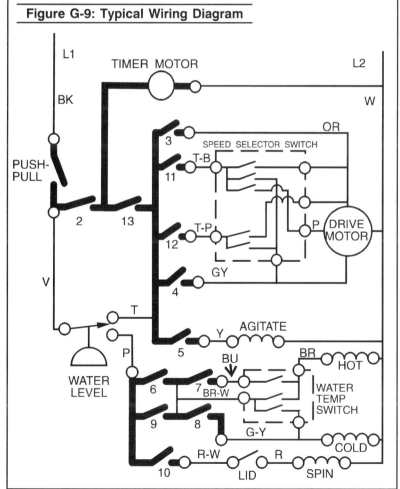

Figure G-9: Typical Wiring Diagram

the violet wire to the water level switch (which must have a LOW water level,) then through the pink wire back into the timer. Inside the timer, it goes through switch number 10. It then comes out of the timer in a red wire with a white stripe (R-W) that leads to the lid switch (which must be closed.) From the lid switch, it goes through a red wire to the spin solenoid. Finally it leaves the spin solenoid in a white wire, which leads back to the main power cord (L2).

If you're not sure whether a certain switch or component is a part of the circuit you're diagnosing, *assume* that it is and test it. For example, switches 3,4,11&12 all lead to the motor circuit. If you have a motor problem that you think you've traced to the timer, don't bother trying to figure out which switch goes to which part of the motor. Test all four; if any of the four switches is bad, you will need to replace the whole timer, anyway.

To test for the break in the circuit, simply isolate each part of the system (remove the wires from the terminals) and test for continuity. For example, to test the spin solenoid in our example, pull the red and white wires off the spin solenoid and test continuity across the solenoid terminals as described in section 2-6(a).

The push-pull switch, and switch number 10 are shown in bold lines, so they are inside the timer. Looking at the diagram, the push-pull switch controls a lot of other things besides the spin solenoid. Since those things are working O.K., we know that the push-pull switch can't be the problem.

For now, let's ignore switch num-

ber 10. (Remember: the timer is the *last* thing you should check; see section 2-5(c).)

That leaves the water level switch, the lid switch, the spin solenoid itself, and the wiring.

Nine times out of ten, a component has gone bad. Test those first. Take power off the machine and check each switch and/or solenoid in the circuit as described in sections 2-5 (a) thru (e).

To check for a wire break, you would pull each end of a wire off the component and test for continuity through it. You may need to use jumpers to extend the wire; for example, if one end of the wire is in the control console and the other end in underneath the machine. If there is no continuity, there is a break in the wire! It will then be up to you to figure out exactly where that break is; there is no magic way. If you have a broken wire, look along the length of

Figure G-9(a): Tracing the Spin Solenoid Circuit

the wire for pinching or chafing. If there is a place where the wires move (like near the wigwag of a belt-driven Whirlpool/Kenmore,) check there first. Even if the insulation is O.K., the wire may be broken inside.

INTERLOCKS

Certain safety mechanisms are installed on almost every washer that can lead you to a misdiagnosis if you forget about them.

For example, a Whirlpool washer will pump out water if the lid is open, but it won't spin. So you've just replaced the pump, and you're standing there with the lid open, admiring how well it's pumping out, when you notice it still isn't spinning. You dive right back into the back of the washer, trying to figure out what you forgot to replace...and the only problem is that the lid is up. Don't laugh; I'd hate to admit to you how many times *I've* done it.

When diagnosing an electrical problem, there are many interlocks in the system that you need to check. (See section 2-7 below.) For example, if your basket won't spin at all, you will check all the obvious stuff (lid switch, spin clutch solenoid, transmission, etc.) But will you think to check the imbalance switch? If it fails, it will have the same effect as a failed lid switch. When tracing an electrical problem, check your wiring diagram to see if there may be any forgotten switches in the malfunctioning system.

Here are a few of the more common safety interlock mechanisms to watch out for:

LID SWITCH: Mentioned above, it prevents the basket from spinning while the washer lid is open. In some designs, it also prevents the tub from filling or the agitator from agitating while the lid is open. See the note about mercury lid switches in section 2-2.

IMBALANCE INTERLOCK: If the washer has detected a substantial imbalance in the load during the spin cycle, the motor will stop. Usually a buzzer will sound. To reset this interlock, the lid must be opened and closed or the timer turned off and back on. (Presumably, you will redistribute the clothes, but it is not necessary to reset the interlock.)

WATER LEVEL INTERLOCK: On some washers, the basket will not start spinning until the water is nearly pumped out of the tub. The start of the spin cycle is dependent on the pump pumping out water and the water level switch sensing that the water level is low enough.

CAUTION: NEVER BYPASS A SAFETY INTERLOCK. THEY ARE THERE FOR A REASON!

2-6(a) SWITCHES AND SOLENOIDS

Testing switches and solenoids is pretty straightforward. Take all wires off the component and test resistance across it.

Switches should show good continuity when closed and no continuity when open.

Solenoids should show SOME resistance, but continuity should be good. If a solenoid shows no continuity, there's a break somewhere in the windings. If it shows no resistance, it's shorted.

2-6(b) WATER LEVEL SWITCHES

Water level diaphragm switches are usually shown on a wiring diagram by the symbol in figure G-10. The numbering or lettering of the terminals may differ, but basically all switches are tested the same way.

To test the switch, first fill the tub to the highest water level. Unplug the machine and set the water level switch on the lowest water level setting. Remove the three leads from the switch. Label the wires to make sure you get them back on the proper terminals.

In the example shown in figure G-10, a check for continuity should show the following:

TUB FULL: No continuity from V to P, continuity from V to T.

Re-attach the wires, plug in the machine and set the timer on "spin" or "drain." When the tub is pumped dry, stop the spin cycle and unplug the washer. Remove the wires from the water level switch and test continuity again. With an empty tub, the continuity should be reversed:

TUB EMPTY: Continuity from V to P, no continuity from V to T.

If you do not get these readings, the water level switch is bad, or there's a leak in the air pressure tube leading to it (as described in section 2-2.) Replace the switch or tube.

The labelling of the three water level switch leads is different in just about every brand, but the switch is tested in the same way.

Figure G-10: Water level Switch Schematic

Tub Full   Tub Empty

2-6(c) TIMERS

The timer is the brain of the washer. It controls everything in the cycle. In addition to telling the motor when and which way to run, it tells any clutch solenoids when to engage, the fill valve when to open, dispenser solenoids when to open, etc.

Most washers still have mechanical, that is, motor-operated timers. Some newer machines have digital timers and control (computer) boards.

Diagnosing digital machines is often a matter of reading the digital fault code or performing a self test. Testing procedures and fault codes for individual models can usually be found on a paper located inside the console.

A mechanical timer is nothing more than a motor that drives a set of cams which open and close switches. Yet it is one of the most expensive parts in your washer, so don't be too quick to diagnose it as the problem. Usually the FIRST thing a layman looks at is the timer; it should be the LAST. And don't forget that timers are electrical parts, which are usually non-returnable. If you buy one, and it turns out *not* to be the problem, you've just wasted the money.

In a wiring diagram, a mechanical timer may appear in two different ways (Figure G-11). The wiring and switches that are inside the timer will either be drawn with dark lines, or there will be a shaded or dotted line drawn around the timer's internal wiring and switches.

DIAGNOSIS

If the timer is not advancing, well, that's pretty obvious. Replace the timer or timer drive motor, or have it rebuilt as described below.

Timers can be difficult to diagnose. The easiest way is to go through everything else in the system that's malfunctioning. If none of the other components are bad, then it may be the timer.

Remember that a timer is simply a set of on-off switches. The switches are turned off and on by a cam, which is driven by the timer motor. Timer wires are color-coded or number-coded.

Let's say you've got a spin solenoid problem that you think you've traced to your timer. First unplug the machine. Look at your wiring diagram and see which internal timer switch feeds the spin solenoid. (See figure G-12) In this case, the pink colored wire and the red colored wire with a white stripe lead to switch #10 inside the timer. REMOVE those wires from the timer and touch the test leads to those terminals. Make sure the timer is in the "on" position and slowly turn the timer all the way through a full cycle. (On some timers, you cannot turn the dial while it is on. Whirl-

pool Direct Drive models (chapter 4) are this way. You must simply test the timer one click at a time. Be patient!)

You should see continuity make and break at least once in the cycle; usually many times. If it doesn't, the internal contacts are bad; replace the timer.

A *special* timer problem occurs only in machines with direct-reversing motors. The symptoms are that when you open the lid at the end of the cycle, the tub hasn't drained. You hear the motor running throughout the cycle, but it doesn't spin or drain; you may also notice that you hear it *agitating* when it's supposed to be *spinning*.

For the motor to reverse, the timer must interrupt power to it for a moment. When the timer gets worn, this simply doesn't happen. The motor doesn't get a chance to start in the opposite direction, so it continues to run in the same direction (agitate) until something interrupts the circuit and

Figure G-11: Typical Timer Schematic

stops the motor. Like *you*, lifting the lid. You can see how the symptoms might appear to be intermittent and a bit confusing. The solution: replace the timer.

In general, timers cannot be rebuilt by the novice. Check with your parts dealer; if it *can* be rebuilt, he'll get it done for you. If it's a common one, your parts dealer may even have a rebuilt one in stock.

For the most part, if your timer is acting up, you need to replace it. To replace, mark the wires or note the color codes written on the timer. If you need to, you can draw a picture of the terminal arrangement and wire colors. If possible, change over the timer wires one-by-one; it can be easier. If there are any special wiring changes, they will be explained in instructions that come with the new timer.

2-6(d) SPEED SELECTOR AND WATER TEMPERATURE SWITCHES

The internal wiring for these switches is almost always shown with a shaded or dotted box around them (Figure G-13.)

The lettering inside the box will tell you what terminals to test. For example, with the temperature switch shown in figure G-13 set on "Warm wash, Cold rinse" all the switches marked with a "WC" will be closed. Take power off the machine, and remove all four wires from the switch. Test for continuity between the BU and the BR terminals; you should see good continuity. Test also between the BR-W and G-Y terminals. You should see good continuity.

Now test between the BR-W and BR terminals. There is no WC marking

Figure G-12: Testing Switches Inside the Timer

next to the middle switch, so the switch should be open. You should see *no* continuity with your VOM. Test the switch similarly for all settings.

2-6(e) DRIVE MOTORS, START SWITCH, AND CAPACITORS

A motor that is trying to start, but can't for whatever reason, is using one heckuva lot of electricity. So much, in fact, that if it is allowed to continue being energized in a stalled state, it will start burning wires. To prevent this, an overload switch is installed on motors to cut power to them if they don't start within a certain amount of time.

If the motor is trying to start, but can't, you will hear certain things. First will be a click, followed immediately by a buzzing or "growling" sound. Then, after about 5 to 20 seconds of this

sound, another click and the sound will stop. The sounds will keep repeating every minute or two. In some extreme cases, you may even smell burning.

If you hear the motor doing this, but it won't start, disconnect power and take all the load off it. For example, disconnect the drive belt, pump drive system, etc.

Try to start the motor again. If it still won't start, the motor, starting capacitor or speed selector switch is bad. (The speed selector switch may be trying to start the motor in two different speeds at once.) If you have an ammeter, a stalled motor will be drawing 10 to 20 amps or more. Replace the bad component.

If the motor DOES start with the load removed, the pump or transmission may be locked up; See section 2-3 and 2-4(a).

Figure G-13: Typical Selector Switch

CAPACITOR

Not all machines have external motor starting capacitors.

On machines that do, most external capacitors are mounted piggyback on the motor. (Figure G-14) A few machines have their capacitors mounted separately inside the cabinet, and a few have them mounted in other places, like behind the control console. See the chapter about *your* machine for details.

If your machine has an external capacitor, unplug the machine and DISCHARGE THE CAPACITOR. BE CAREFUL; IT CAN GIVE YOU A NASTY SHOCK, *EVEN IF THE WASHER IS NOT PLUGGED IN!* You can discharge it by shorting the two terminals on your capacitor with your screwdriver. Be careful not to touch the metal part of your screwdriver with your hands while you do this.

After discharging the capacitor, disconnect its leads and test it. Set your VOM on Rx1 and touch the two test probes to the two capacitor terminals. Initially, the meter should bounce towards the right of the scale (good continuity), then slowly move back to the left side a bit as the capacitor builds resistance. Reverse the two probes on the terminals. The meter reading should act the same way. If you do not get these readings, replace the capacitor.

STARTING SWITCH

Old-style GE-built machines have an external, replaceable current-relay starting switch. See the GE chapter for testing.

Most other machines have a *centrifugal* starting switch mounted piggyback on the motor. Testing the switch is most easily accomplished by replacing it.

Remember that starting switches are electrical parts, which are generally not returnable. If you test the switch by replacing it, and the problem turns out to be the motor itself, you will probably not be able to return the starting switch for a refund. But they're generally pretty cheap, and if it IS the problem, you just saved yourself the best part of a hundred bucks for a new motor.

MOTOR

If your motor is stalled (buzzing and/or tripping out on the overload switch) and the capacitor, starting switch and speed selector switches test O.K., the motor is bad. Replace it.

Figure G-14: Piggyback Capacitor

Drive Motor

Capacitor

Chapter 3

OLD-STYLE GENERAL ELECTRIC
including Hotpoint & JC Penney

NOTE: Chapter 2 covers problems common to both GE washer designs. THIS chapter covers only diagnosis and repairs peculiar to pre-1995 machines. If you do not read Chapter 2 thoroughly before you read this chapter, you probably will not be able to properly diagnose your machine!!!!

3-1 BASIC OPERATION

The old-style GE design uses a single-speed reversing motor, which is belted to the transmission. When viewed from the top, the motor turns clockwise for the agitation cycle, and counterclockwise for the spin cycle (Figure GE-1.)

A simple centrifugal clutch prevents the motor from taking heavy shock loads when starting. Some models have a two-speed clutch (only the clutch is two-speed, not the motor.) The second speed is slower, for "gentle" cycles, and is solenoid-activated.

Figure GE-1: Drive Train

Agitator Drive Shaft

Spin Tube

Basket Mounting Flange

Transmission

Pump

Pump Coupling

Clutch

Drive Belt

Drive Motor

The pump is also direct-reversing. It is connected directly to the motor through a flexible coupling. Most GE pumps have two impellers and four hose connections. One impeller recirculates water during the wash and rinse cycles, and the other pumps water out of the tub during the spin cycle.

3-2 OPENING THE CABINET AND CONSOLE

See Figure GE-2 for details about opening the cabinet and console.

In raising the top of the cabinet, you must keep two things in mind:

1) It is better to use a putty knife, rather than a screwdriver, to push the catches. There is less chance of chipping or scratching the finish.

2) Inside the lid, on the top right side, is the recirculation nozzle. (see figure GE-7) The nozzle fits through a hole in the soft plastic skirt attached to the top of the cabinet. You must push the nozzle out of the skirt as you raise the cabinet top, and insert the nozzle back through the skirt when you lower it.

Most GE machines have a wiring diagram in an envelope inside the console.

3-3 WHAT TYPICALLY GOES WRONG WITH THESE MACHINES

Since the operating system is so simple, the easiest way to diagnose a mechanical problem is to open up the back of the washer and observe things while you run the washer through its cycles. Following are the most common problems:

Figure GE-2: Cabinet and Console Access

To Access Timer or other console switches, remove these four screws

To lift cabinet top:
Push on spring catches here with putty knife

Cabinet Top
Spring Catch
Cabinet
putty knife blade
CROSS-SECTION

REAR OF WASHER

To Access Pump, Snubbers, Motor Relay or Drive Train, remove screws holding on the fiberboard panel

SYMPTOM: WATER LEAKS

See section 2-4 on leaks and backed up drains.

Besides the usual loose or worn hoses and fill system problems, leaks in these washers most commonly come from one of five places:

1) Look at the pump through the back of the washer. There is a small inspection hole (figure GE-4) in the pump body that weeps water when the pump's internal seal is leaking. You may not see any water directly, but you will see its tracks leading down the pump body. See section 3-4 on pumps.

2) These washers are quite different from others in that the tub is attached to the cabinet, rather than the transmission. If there is an imbalance, only the basket and drive train wobbles; not the whole tub. (See Figure GE-3)

Between the transmission and tub, there is a large flexible rubber seal called a boot. This boot can get brittle and crusted with detergent. It can develop leaks, or even shake loose, causing a MASSIVE leak (during the fill cycle, the water dumps straight onto the floor instead of filling the tub). Look for water coming from around the top of the transmission. See section 3-6.

3) Since the basket is free to move around in the tub, the basket may hit the tub if there is too large an imbalance. If this happens too often, it can actually wear a hole in the tub. Usually such holes will appear around the top of the tub. If you have holes worn in

the tub, you can sometimes patch them with an epoxy patch kit, available at your appliance parts dealer. It may prove to be a temporary repair, but you can always do it again, and it's cheaper than trashing the washer. I also recommend an excellent product called Slapstix. It is a plastic abrasion-resistant patch kit made specifically for GE washers. As of this writing, it is not yet widely available, but ask your dealer or call 800-936-5282.

4) The tub fittings may leak. If you detect a leak from the tub drain or other tub fitting, remove the basket as described in section 3-6.

5) You may get a calcium or detergent buildup around the fill or recirculation nozzle. Such a buildup can cause the nozzle to spray water over the top of the tub. Clean out or replace the nozzle.

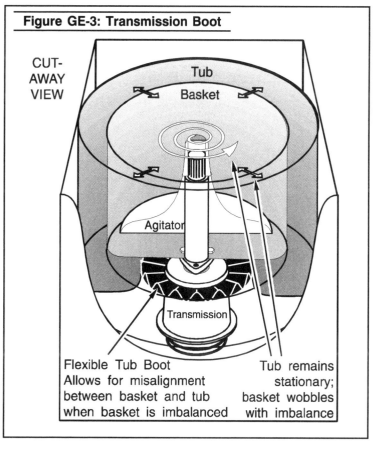

Figure GE-3: Transmission Boot

CUT-AWAY VIEW

Tub

Basket

Agitator

Transmission

Flexible Tub Boot
Allows for misalignment
between basket and tub
when basket is imbalanced

Tub remains
stationary;
basket wobbles
with imbalance

SYMPTOM: BASKET SPINS, BUT WATER DOESN'T DRAIN FROM TUB.

Usually the pump has gone belly up. Replace it as described in section 3-4.

If the machine is not pumping out water because the coupling has come off the pump, check the pump for jamming. See section 3-4.

SYMPTOM: SLOW OR NO AGITATE AND/OR SPIN.

When diagnosing this problem, keep in mind that the pump is coupled directly to the motor; it does not receive power through the clutch. Only the transmission receives power through the clutch and belt. Therefore, a locked transmission *will not* stop the motor from turning, but a locked pump *will*.

1) If NOTHING on the machine works, and it's not even making any noise, check the power supply. Also check the electrical components in section 2-6.

NOTE: In some models, the lid switch stops the machine completely. In others, only the spin cycle is interlocked, and the machine will still fill and agitate with the lid raised. Check your wiring diagram.

2) The belt may be broken or loose. Check as described in section 2-5(a) and tighten or replace as described in section 3-10.

3) Often a sock or something has jammed in the pump. This symptom is often accompanied by a strong burning smell. You will also hear the motor trying to start, then tripping off by the motor overload switch, because it is being stalled by the pump. An additional confirmation of this diagnosis is that if you look at the pump coupling while the motor is trying to start, it will be twisted tightly. See section 3-4.

4) If the transmission pulley is turning, but either agitate or spin or both are not working, the transmission is bad. Replace as described in section 3-13.

If the pump is turning, but the transmission drive pulley is not turning, stop the washer and disconnect power. Try turning the transmission pulley by hand, in both directions. If the transmission pulley will not turn in one or both directions, the transmission needs to be replaced. See section 3-13.

Figure GE-4: Pump

Water Relief Hole

Pump Coupling Plate

If the transmission pulley turns fairly easily by hand, but the clutch drum is turning slowly or not at all under motor power, the clutch may be bad. Usually there will be a loud rattling noise. See section 3-11.

5) The motor or starting solenoid may be burnt out. Remember that the motor *may* start in one direction, but not in the other. Usually you will hear the motor buzzing as it tries to start, then dropping out on the overload. Check as described in section 3-12.

6) If the washer spins but does not agitate, check the agitator splines. Section 3-5.

7) If you have a two-speed machine and the slow (gentle) speed is not working, the clutch solenoid may not be working. See section 3-11.

SYMPTOM: BASKET SPINS (CLOCKWISE) WHILE AGITATING.

The transmission needs to be replaced. See section 3-13.

Figure GE-5: Pump Coupling

Pump Coupling Clamp

Motor Coupling Clamp

SYMPTOM: OIL LEAKS

A little bit of oil leakage is normal. If oil is leaking so badly that it is slinging off the transmission drive pulley and getting around the inside of the cabinet, you will need to replace the transmission as described in section 3-13.

SYMPTOM: EXCESSIVE NOISE OR VIBRATION

A whining or loud clattering noise is usually a worn clutch. See section 3-11.

If the machine makes a squeaking noise, especially during the spin cycle, the snubbers are probably worn out. This is especially true if the machine has difficulty balancing during spin, even after you redistribute the clothes. Replace the snubber blocks as described in section 3-14.

3-4 PUMP AND PUMP COUPLING

A vast majority of GE-built washers use the pump shown in figure GE-4. A few less-expensive models used a non-recirculating pump with only two hose connections.

The pump is connected directly to the motor through a rubber/fabric flexible coupling (Figure GE-5.) The pump coupling is connected to both by a round clamp at each end. When installing a new coupling, do not remove the staples that hold it in shape. Also, put the gaps in the clamps directly over the gaps in the coupling.

If the pump seal is leaking, you will see water weeping (or the tracks of a water weep) from the hole shown in figure GE-4.

There are no special tricks to replacing a GE pump. First, drain the tub as described in section 1-6. Disconnect the pump coupling at the TOP end, then the remove the three pump mounting screws. Have a bucket ready to catch water, and remove the four pump hoses.

Installation is the opposite of removal.

If something is jamming the pump, the pump coupling will be twisted tightly while the motor is trying to start. Check for jams as described in section 2-3.

If the pump is not turning freely, but you cannot find a jam, replace the pump.

If the coupling has come off the pump, make sure you check that the pump is turning freely.

3-5 AGITATOR

Most GE-designed agitators are not fastened to the shaft by any screws or bolts. To remove, simply tug upwards on the bottom of the agitator. There are exceptions; see "handwash" agitators below.

If you find that you cannot remove the agitator by pulling on it, try tapping the top of the agitator gently with a rubber or wooden mallet. If you *still* cannot remove the agitator, pry off the plastic cap in the center. Then cut out the little piece of plastic in the center of the hub with a knife; this will expose the top of the agitator shaft. (Figure GE-6) Hit it with a little WD-40 to loosen it.

GE-designed agitators have a removable rubber spline insert that connects the agitator to the transmission shaft splines (Figure GE-6.) If the splines are stripped, you can replace the whole agitator, or just the rubber spline insert.

To remove the insert, remove the plastic cap and cut out the center plastic piece as described above. Push out the old spline insert (it can be difficult.) To replace, put the new insert onto the top of the transmission shaft and push the agitator down onto it.

Hotpoint and JC Penney have a "handwash" agitator on some designs. The "handwash" agitator is actually a small agitator that fits inside the larger, main agitator. The "handwash" agitator has a small screw underneath the metal disc on top of the agitator; make sure you remove it

Figure GE-6: Agitator Hub

To remove a stuck agitator, Pry off cap and (in some models) cut out center piece.

Rubber Spline Insert connects Agitator Shaft to Agitator

before trying to pull up on the "handwash" agitator. There are locking tabs that you must twist to remove the larger agitator from the smaller one.

Once the screw is removed, the "handwash" agitator should lift out easily. If not, tap with a rubber mallet a described above, or shoot some WD-40 into the screw hole.

3-6 TUB BOOT SEAL AND TUB FITTINGS

To access the transmission boot or replace tub fittings, you must remove the basket.

Drain the tub, raise the cabinet top, and remove the agitator as described in section 3-5. Remove the recirculation nozzle (figure GE-7) by simply pulling it straight out. Remove the agitator bushing by pressing on the spring-loaded tab. Beneath the agitator bushing are three basket mounting bolts. (Figure GE-8.) Remove the three bolts with a 1/2-inch 12-point socket or box wrench and lift out the basket.

Figure GE-7: Recirculation Nozzle Removal

To remove recirculation nozzle, pull it straight out of its rubber mount

Tub

Basket

Agitator

VIEW:
Front of Washer
Cabinet Top Raised

Figure GE-8: Agitator Bushing and Basket Mounting Bolts

Push tab to remove agitator bushing.

To remove basket, remove three bolts with a 1/2-inch, 12-point socket or box wrench.

Spin Tube

Agitator Bushing

Basket Bolts

VIEW: Bottom of Basket
with Agitator Removed

NOTE: ONLY USE A 12-POINT WRENCH ON THESE BASKET BOLTS. DO NOT ATTEMPT TO USE A 6-POINT WRENCH ON THEM.

The tub boot and all tub fittings will now be visible. (Figure GE-9) IF THE TUB BOOT IS NOT LEAKING, DO NOT REMOVE IT. If you need to remove it, it is simply clamped to the transmission top and to a lip on the tub by two big round clamps. If it has simply shaken loose and not torn, you can just clamp the old one back in place, but you'd better check the snubber blocks as described in section 3-14 to try to find out why it shook loose in the first place.

Re-assembly is the opposite of disassembly.

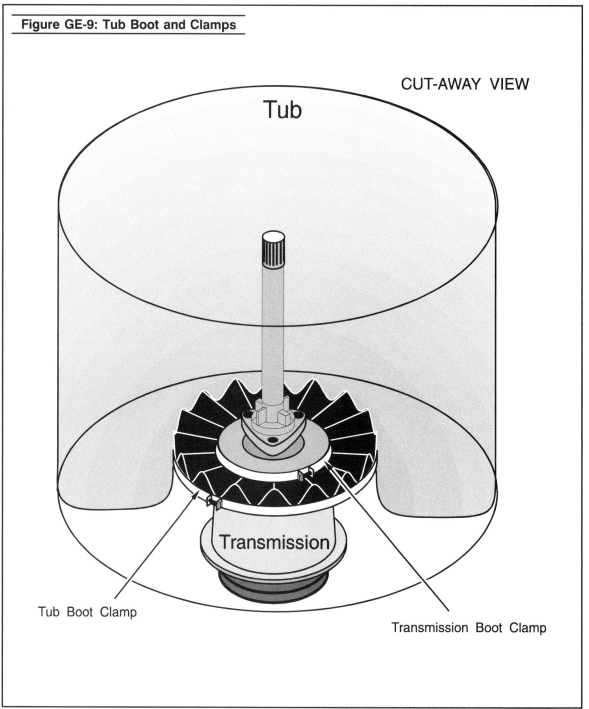

Figure GE-9: Tub Boot and Clamps

CUT-AWAY VIEW

Tub

Transmission

Tub Boot Clamp

Transmission Boot Clamp

3-7 TIMER

Testing the timer is described in section 2-6(c).

To test or remove the timer, remove the console as described in section 3-2. If the timer dial prevents you from removing the timer, pull off the spring clip from behind the timer knob as shown in figure GE-10. Mark the timer wires as you remove them, or better yet, pull the wires off the old timer and put them directly on the new one, one at a time.

GE used two basic timer designs over the years. One used a metal housing. The other design is known as a "clamshell" timer because of the curved shape of its plastic housing. Both are rebuildable, though not by a novice. If your timer is defective, take it to your parts dealer and ask for a rebuilt.

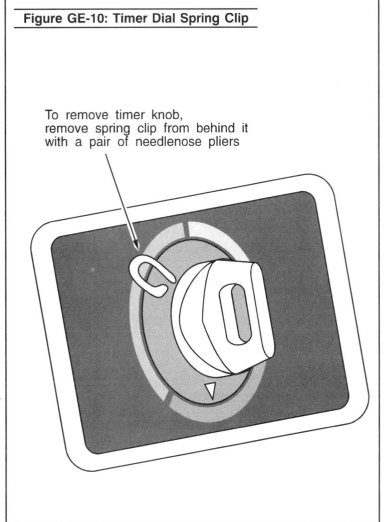

Figure GE-10: Timer Dial Spring Clip

To remove timer knob, remove spring clip from behind it with a pair of needlenose pliers

Figure GE-11: Water Level Switch Schematic

May be labelled 7, 1, or V

May be labelled 16, 3, or T

May be labelled 15, 2, or P

3-8 LID SWITCH

The lid switch is located beneath the cabinet top, towards the right rear of the washer. It is a simple, mechanically-activated switch. Test with an ohmmeter and replace if defective.

3-9 WATER LEVEL SWITCH

The water level switch is located beneath the console. GE washers used several different wiring schemes, so refer to section 2-6(b) and compare with figure GE-11 to determine which terminals to test. If the switch is bad, replace it.

3-10 BELT

Remove power from the washer and remove the back panel as described in section 3-2.

To tension the belt, loosen the three motor mounting bolts on the underside of the motor mounting plate. Proper tension is when the belt can be deflected approximately 1/2-inch, midway between the motor and transmission pulleys, with your fingers. Use your hands; you do not need any extra leverage on the motor to set proper belt tension.

To replace the belt, simply remove the upper pump coupling and install the new belt.

3-11 CLUTCH

GE washers use two different clutches (Figure GE-12.)

The two-speed clutch can be identified by the solenoid that activates the slow speed. It also has a larger outer clutch drum. If the slow (gentle) agitator speed is not working, test the solenoid coil for continuity. If it has no continuity, replace by removing the screw on the underside of the coil.

I do not recommend the novice trying to rebuild a two-speed clutch. They are complex assemblies; difficult to disassemble, assemble, and adjust. If you suspect your two-speed clutch assem-

Figure GE-12: Clutches

Two-Speed has
1) a solenoid on the side, and
2) a slightly larger drum, with cut-outs in the skirt

Pump Coupling Plate

Belt Pulley

Low Speed Solenoid

Clutch Drum

Solenoid Leads

TWO-SPEED CLUTCH   SINGLE-SPEED CLUTCH

bly is bad, remove the motor and clutch assembly from the machine and take the assembly to a rebuilder.

On the other hand, a single-speed clutch is a relatively simple assembly. To service the single-speed clutch, first remove power from the washer and remove the back panel. Disconnect the pump coupling, loosen the motor mounting bolts, and remove the drive belt. Disconnect the motor wiring at the terminal block. Remove the motor mounting bolts (be careful; the motor is heavy!) and remove the motor and clutch assembly from the washer.

Figure GE-13: Pump Coupling Plate Removal

Pump Coupling Plate

Motor Shaft Extension

Clutch Drum

Using a straight punch, drive the roll pin out of the motor shaft extension. You can then easily lift off the pump coupling plate.

Roll Pin

There is a roll pin in the pump coupling plate on top of the clutch pulley. Drive it out with a straight punch. (Figure GE-13.) Lift off the pump coupling plate.

Lift off the clutch drum. If it does not lift off easily, tap lightly on the motor shaft extension with a hammer. If that doesn't get it off, you will need to use a wheel puller and horseshoe collar.

CAUTION: If you use a wheel puller to remove the clutch drum, do not pull on the skirt of the drum. Use a horseshoe collar (Figure GE-14) to pull on the drive pulley.

Figure GE-14: Horseshoe Collar

Wheel Puller

Horseshoe Collar

Clutch Drum Skirt

Put Horseshoe Collar around belt pulley and remove clutch drum with wheel puller.

NOTE: DO NOT USE THE WHEEL PULLER DIRECTLY ON THE SKIRT OF THE CLUTCH DRUM. YOU MAY BEND, OR POSSIBLY EVEN BREAK IT!

See figure GE-15 for disassembly of the clutch components. Inspect the shoes and clutch drum for excessive wear. If you're not sure if the shoes can be re-used, ask your appliance parts dealer, or simply replace them. They're cheap insurance against future problems.

Normally you will not need to remove the shaft extension, but do inspect it, and replace if worn or damaged.

Reassembly is the opposite of disassembly. To get the roll pin in, line up the holes and stick in a nail to keep the holes aligned. Then drive the pin in from the opposite side as the nail.

Figure GE-15: Single Speed Clutch (Exploded View)

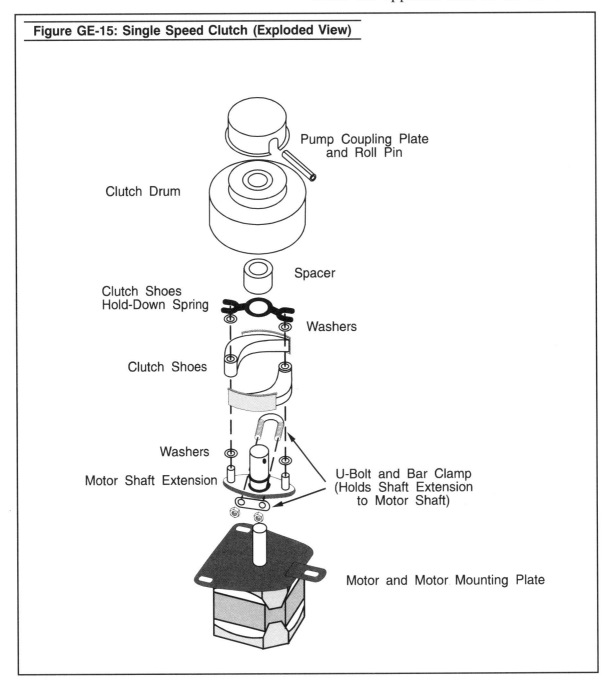

Pump Coupling Plate and Roll Pin

Clutch Drum

Spacer

Clutch Shoes Hold-Down Spring

Washers

Clutch Shoes

Washers

Motor Shaft Extension

U-Bolt and Bar Clamp (Holds Shaft Extension to Motor Shaft)

Motor and Motor Mounting Plate

3-12 MOTOR AND RELAY

If you hear the motor trying to start, but dropping out on the motor overload, and the pump coupling is not twisted when the motor is trying to start, either the relay is defective or a motor winding is burnt out. Test as described below.

RELAY

GE washers use a separate relay. Remove the back panel. As you look at the back of the machine, you will find the relay towards the upper left side of the machine. (Figure GE-16)

To test the relay, first remove power from the machine. Mark the relay wires and remove them. Remove the relay from the machine.

With your ohmmeter set on Rx1, test between the terminals marked "M" and "LS." You should see *good* continuity.

Test between the terminals marked "L" and "S." You should see *no* continuity.

Turn the relay *UPSIDE DOWN* and test again between the "L" and "S" terminals. You should now see *good* continuity.

If you do not get the above readings, replace the relay. It is very important to get the right relay; it matches the motor that's installed.

MOTOR

If the relay is not bad, the motor is. Replace the motor and relay as a pair. Make sure you get the right motor for your machine. The motor mount is held in place by three nuts.

Figure GE-16: Motor Starting Relay

Look for Relay Here

Terminals

Motor Start Relay

VIEW:
Rear of Washer, Back Panel Removed

3-13 TRANSMISSION

To replace the transmission, first remove the basket and tub boot as described in section 3-6.

Remove the six transmission mounting bolts shown in figure GE-17. Slide the transmission towards the right rear of the washer, and reach under the transmission to make sure the drive belt has disengaged from it. Lift out the transmission (be careful; it is heavy.)

The transmission can be rebuilt, but not by the novice. Rebuilt GE transmissions are a standard item at most parts stores, and they are not terribly expensive. Make sure you get the right shaft length.

Replacement is the opposite of removal. Lower the transmission into place, and slip the drive belt on. Locate the right rear bolt loosely in its hole, then the left front bolt, then the other four.

Install the boot, basket, and agitator. As a final step, remove the back from the washer and make sure the belt is seated properly.

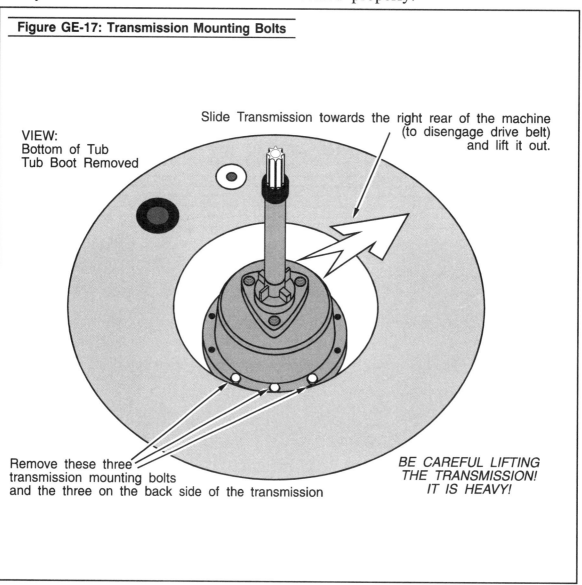

Figure GE-17: Transmission Mounting Bolts

Slide Transmission towards the right rear of the machine (to disengage drive belt) and lift it out.

VIEW:
Bottom of Tub
Tub Boot Removed

Remove these three transmission mounting bolts and the three on the back side of the transmission

BE CAREFUL LIFTING THE TRANSMISSION! IT IS HEAVY!

3-14 SNUBBER BLOCKS

There are eight friction pads, commonly known as snubber blocks, which help to prevent vibration during the spin cycle. There are two in each corner of the machine. (Figure GE-18) These can wear out, causing excessive vibration and a squeaking noise. Often they will be missing when you look for them. Lift the spring and replace them. Be careful not to catch your fingers under the spring.

Figure GE-18: Snubber Blocks

VIEW:
Rear of Washer,
Back Panel Removed

There are eight snubber blocks total;
two in each corner of the washer.

CLOSE-UP VIEW

Snubber Block

Snubber Block

Snubber Block

To remove or replace snubber block,
pull spring away from block.

CAUTION: SNUBBER BLOCK SPRING IS VERY STRONG! BE CAREFUL NOT TO PINCH YOUR FINGERS!

Chapter 4

GE FRONT-ACCESS MACHINES
including Hotpoint, JC Penney & RCA

NOTE: Chapter 2 covers problems common to both GE washer designs. THIS chapter covers only diagnosis and repairs peculiar to post-1995 machines. If you do not read Chapter 2 thoroughly before you read this chapter, you probably will not be able to properly diagnose your machine!!!!

In 1995, GE began manufacturing a new washing machine. They are commonly referred to as the "front-access" or "easy-access" machines, or simply the "new-style" GE washer, versus the "old-style" machine. GE sells them under several brands and model names, including "Profile" and "Maxus."

Except for the drain hose, everything is easily serviceable from the front of the machine.

Inside the console, there is a "mini-manual" containing condensed disassembly instructions and a wiring diagram.

4-1 OPERATING SYSTEM

These machines are direct-reversing. The drive motor drives the transmission through a clutch and a belt. The belt is the same one used in the old machine. The basket is attached directly to the transmission, which itself spins during the spin cycle. When the motor stops or reverses, a brake attached to the bottom of the transmission engages, keeping the transmission from turning during agitation. (Figure FA-1)

There is no pump-driven water recirculation. Flexible fins on the agitator circulate water in the tub and through the self-cleaning lint filter in the basket hub.

Figure FA-1: Drive Train

The brake assembly is attached to the transmission and brakes against the motor platform. When the brake releases, the transmission rotates and the basket spins.

Agitator Shaft

Top of Transmission casing is attached to basket

Direct-Reversing Drive Motor

Counter-weight

Transmission

Brake

Clutch   Belt   Lower Bearing

Ball bearings in ramped tracks in the lower bearing engage and release the brake when the motor reverses.

One of the features is that the drive motor does not drive the pump. The drain pump in these machines is a separate unit with its' own motor.

The suspension in these machines is reported to be VERY good. In one videotaped demo I saw, they put eight pounds of phone books in the machine during the spin cycle and the thing barely vibrated. In fact, if the washer is dancing around during the spin cycle, whoever installed the machine probably forgot to remove the suspension rod, inserted to keep the tub from moving during shipping. (It's a long rod, almost the width of the machine, that you pull out of a hole on the bottom right side of the cabinet.) The suspension system is supplemented by a liquid-filled (unserviceable) balance ring in the top of the basket.

Some customers have complained about the pump being too loud. On the higher-end models, GE put some sound deadening insulation in the cabinet, but if you don't have one of these machines, there is an insulation kit available with panels that stick on the inside of the cabinet.

A few more tidbits of info about these machines:

1) All functions are interlocked through the lid switch except the fill cycle. The washer will not agitate, drain or spin with the lid open.

2) There is a pre-pump function built into the water level switch. The water level must be quite low before the water level switch will allow the basket to start spinning.

Most of the parts on these machines are designed to be thrown away. For example, the transmission is a tiny little thing that was designed in large part around EPA requirements (less than 3 ounces of oil, stuff like that.) It was NOT designed with rebuilding in mind.

4-2 WHAT TYPICALLY GOES WRONG WITH THESE MACHINES

SYMPTOM: WATER LEAKS

A very common problem with these machines is that the drain hose, which is made of plastic instead of rubber, cracks and leaks. The triangle bracket that holds it on is a separate item and is very difficult to get off the hose. Replace the hose and the triangle bracket with it. (Figure FA-2)

If you think water may be leaking from the seal between the tub and transmission, see section 4-5.

They have also been experiencing some drain pump leaks. Replace the pump.

Another common complaint is that water mysteriously leaks during the agitate cycle. What is happening is that the lower transmission ball bearings

Figure FA-2: Drain Hose

End of hose just presses into hose socket

Triangle Bracket secures it in place. It's difficult to remove. Use a new one.

are worn so the brake is not engaging fully. The basket then spins during the agitate cycle and and slings water over the edge of the tub. The basket obviously will not brake properly at the end of the spin cycle either. A lower bearing kit is available to rebuild the lower (ball) bearing assembly. See section 4-5.

SYMPTOM: NO DRAIN

The fan blades on the front of the pump should turn easily by hand. If not, check for something jamming the pump. If it turns easily by hand but won't drain the tub, replace the whole pump and motor assembly. Ditto if the pump leaks. See section 4-4.

SYMPTOM: MOTOR STARTING PROBLEMS AND / OR BLEACH LEAK

Another problem experienced with these machines is with a bleach dispenser / hose installed only on two-speed machines. Besides the fact that bleach is very hard on plastic and rubber parts, such as the hose itself, the hose chafes on one of the suspension rods until a hole develops. (Figure FA-3) Bleach then dribbles out and directly onto the drive motor connectors. The symptom is that the drive motor hums and will not start. There is a replacement wiring harness available; try that first. If the drive motor still won't start, it may need to be replaced. See section 4-4. Incidentally, you won't see this except in the earliest models; when this problem started showing up, GE quickly redesigned the bleach dispenser hose routing.

SYMPTOM: NO SPIN OR AGITATE

The clutches have been experiencing some failures. The problem here is that the clutch pulley is pressed together and the top half of it comes off. You'll find the belt and the top half of the pulley just laying there. Obviously the machine does not agitate or spin.

Another problem experienced, though it doesn't appear to be a widespread problem yet, is that there have been some transmission failures. The symptom is that you attempt to remove the agitator, and the whole agitator shaft comes out with it. A spring clip inside is coming loose. Replace the whole transmission and brake assembly as described in section 4-5.

Figure FA-3: Inside the Cabinet

Motor Wiring Harness Wrapped Around Suspension Rod

Bleach and Water Level Switch Hoses

Bleach Hose Used to run here

Motor Wiring Harness Connection

Suspension Rods

Suspension Dampers

Tub Drain Hose

Drive Motor   Clutch   Drain Pump

4-3 CONSOLE

To access the timer, temperature or water level switches, fill valve, or to remove the cabinet top, you must remove the console. Remove the four #15 torx-head screws on top and the console drops off. You can then pull the terminal blocks off the timer and any other switches in the console and set it aside.

The fill valve is accessible on the left. Unlike water valves of the past, the fill strainer screens are plastic and removable. They have a little tab in the middle that you can grab with a pair of needlenose pliers to remove and clean or replace them.

Unlike switchblocks of the past, the selector switches and water level switch are not held in place by screws. There is a locking tab on each. (Figure FA-4) You pry up the tab with the screwdriver and twist it counterclockwise to remove it. Installation is just

Figure FA-4: Console Switch Removal

To remove switches:
   Pry up tab
 and twist switch
counterclockwise

the opposite; put the switch in place and twist it clockwise until the locking tab clicks.

Unlike the other switches in the panel, timers are held in place by one screw. The timer dial is held to the shaft by a clip. To remove it, pull it until the timer clicks into the "run" position, then reach behind it with a flat screwdriver and poke the clip off. To reinstall it, put the clip on the back of the dial, then line it up and push it onto the timer shaft.

Figure FA-5: Opening the Cabinet

With a putty knife, push in line with the edges of the lid

Lid

Lean the cabinet front forward and lift it off

Disconnect any bleach hose Then remove two screws and slide the cabinet top towards you.

Disconnect lid switch plug before lifting it off.

Unlike the old clamshell timers of the past, these timers are throw-away items; they are not rebuildable. They are also impulse-step timers: you sometimes have to wait two or three minutes for something to happen, unlike the old sequence timers, where you could literally watch them clicking off time.

4-4 CABINET FRONT ACCESS

To access the pump, belt, clutch or drive motor, you need to remove the front panel. The front panel of these machines is held in place by two spring catches at the top, and rests on two tabs at the bottom. Remove as shown in figure FA-5.

Removal of either the drive motor or pump is pretty straightforward. To re-move the belt, loosen the motor mounting bolts to relieve belt tension. In certain positions, the transmission may block the drive motor from coming out. If so, physically turn the transmission until there is clearance.

The whole clutch comes off in one piece as shown in figure FA-6 and is replaced as a unit. The clip that holds the clutch on must be bent to remove it and is not reuseable. Replace.

A short word about the suspension. The two cylinders at the end of the suspension rods are suspension dampers. They contain springs, but they also seal and compress air, much like an air shock on a car. They are color-coded; the front ones are heavier than the back ones, because of the added weight of the motor and clutch.

Figure FA-6: Clutch Removal and Installation

To remove or install clip:
Squeeze and twist
with slip-joint pliers

Remove

Install

Clutch

Drive Motor

Drive Motor

4-5 TUB REMOVAL

Drain the tub (as described in chapter 1.)

To replace the lower bearing or transmission, the tub must be removed.

To replace the waterseal, GE says that it is designed with tabs on it, to enable you to remove it with a pair of pliers, *without removing the tranny.* When I tried it, The tabs were not beefy enough and my pliers kept slipping off them. Without the tranny there, the seal popped off easily with the handle of a pair of pliers. If you need to replace the water seal, take out the basket, try it and decide for yourself.

To remove the tub, first remove the control console as described in section 4-5.

Remove the cabinet front as described in section 4-4.

Remove the cabinet top by removing the screws in the two front corners. The back of the top panel is held on by hooks, so slide it forward and lift it off. Before you remove it completely, disconnect the lid switch wiring harness plug on the right (orange wire & white wire.) Also remove the bleach tube from the front of the cabinet top.

Disconnect the water fill valve and the wiring to it. Remove the 5 screws

Figure FA-7: Agitator Removal & Air Bell

Place belt beneath agitator and tug upwards sharply.
there is a special tool sold for this,
but the belt around your waist will do
(IF you're *thick* enough!)

BE CAREFUL! It comes up fast
and it can pop you in the face!

Basket

Basket Hub with
Self-Cleaning
Lint Filter

Air Bell
(Left-Handed Tub Nut
is underneath)

holding on the backsplash and lift it off; the fill valve will come with it. Remove the screws from the dampening straps (four rubber straps at the top of the tub.)

If you are going to be removing the transmission, remove the agitator and basket. If you are just servicing the lower bearing, skip ahead to "removing the tub and transmission." You do not need to remove the basket, although the tub will be heavier when you remove it with the basket in it)

REMOVING THE AGITATOR AND BASKET

Remove the agitator by slipping a belt underneath it as shown in figure FA-7, and tugging upwards sharply.

Caution: The agitator comes flying outta there pretty fast, and it can hit you in the face if you're not careful.

Remove the bolt and the plastic air bell. Note that besides holding the agitator, the air bell contains air to keep water away from the transmission oil seal. So the O-ring on the bolt that holds the air bell in place is an important air seal and must be in good shape. (figure FA-7)

The basket can be removed by removing the basket nut under the air bell. Note that this is an aluminum, left-handed nut (turn clockwise to unscrew). They are on VERY tight and being aluminum, they are easy to damage. There is a special slugging spanner wrench to remove these nuts; unfortunately, they're not cheap. However, do not use an open end wrench; you WILL damage the nut. Do not heat it either... it is WAY too close to the transmission oil seal.

REMOVING THE TUB AND TRANSMISSION

At this point you can remove the tub crown if you just need to get under the basket. If you're removing the tub, wait till it's out to remove the tub crown & basket. It's a little easier.

Down below in the tub area, disconnect the pressure switch tube from left side of the tub, and bleach hose if installed. Disconnect the tub drain hose at the tub end.

Unplug the wiring harness(es) from motor and unwind from the right suspension rod.

Lift the front of the tub off the suspension rods and snap the brackets out of the motor platform.

Tilt the transmission forward and disengage rear suspension. Careful, it's heavy. Then lift the tub and tilt it either forward or backwards to remove it from the cabinet.

Pop off the eight clips holding on the tub crown. Note that three sides of the crown have forks that fit over knobs on the side of the tub, so it can only go on one way.)

Remove the basket and the split ring and washer underneath it from the top of the transmission casing. When reinstalling, note that the tapered side of the split ring goes upward.

Flip the tub assembly upside down and set it on the ground.

Squeeze the belt with your hand and remove the pulley bolt and the pulley. Note that the ribs on the pulley stick upwards.

The lower bearing assembly is now accessible. A rebuild kit is available for (at the time of this writing) about $75, with the special tools necessary available for about $50 more. See section 4-6 to rebuild.

To remove the transmission, cut the cable tie holding the overflow pipe to the motor platform. Remove the four bolts holding the motor platform to the transmission, and the four bolts holding the platform to the tub. Remove the motor platform and pull the transmission straight out. There is a washer (shim) between the transmission and the tub. The transmission and brake are one unit and are replaced together. The transmission is a throw-away item and is not rebuildable.

The tub bearing is not replaceable; if it is bad you must replace the tub. The water seal is replaceable. Using the handles of a pair of pliers, pop it out from the inside of the tub and press a new one in by hand.

4-6 REBUILDING THE LOWER BEARING (Figure FA-8)

There is a bearing kit to replace the lower bearing. Virtually all the parts shown are thrown away and replaced. There is an adjustment to be made in installing the new bearing. Several different pulley hubs are included in the bearing kit; each is a different thickness. There are metal guages and instructions also included in the bearing kit.

There's also a set of special tools to change it out. They're expensive, but the hub tool (part of the kit) is necessary to make the final adjustment.

Figure FA-8: Lower Bearing

LGS Spring

Pulley Hub

Retainer Ring

Triangle Washer (Flat Side Up)

Cam

Brake Hub with Ball Bearings (Part of the Transmission)

Index

A

Agitation Cycle. *See* **Cycles**
Agitator. *See also* **Individual Model**
  Weak Agitation 2.9
Ammeter 1.4
  How to Use 1.8

B

Belt, Drive
  Broken 2.7, 2.9
Bleach Dispenser. *See* **Dispenser**
Brake 2.2
Burning Smell. *See* **Smell, Burning**

C

Capacitor 2.18
Circuit Board 2.14
Clutch 2.2
Continuity, Testing for 1.7
Control Board 2.14
Cycles 2.1
  Agitate 2.2
  Drain 2.2
  Fill 2.1
  Rinse 2.2
  Spin 2.2
  Wash 2.2

D

Direct-Reversing Motor. *See* **Motor**
Dispenser
  Bleach 2.2
  Fabric Softener 2.2
  Leaks 2.8
Drain Cycle. *See* **Cycles**
Draining the Tub 1.5
Drive Belt. *See* **Belt, Drive**
Drive Motor. *See* **Motor: Drive**

F

Fabric Softener Dispenser. *See* **Dispenser**
Fill Cycle. *See* **Cycles**
Fill Hoses. *See* **Hoses: Fill**
Fill Solenoid Valve. *See* **Solenoid Valve**
Float Switch 2.3

G

General Electric Front Access Machines
  Agitator Removal 4.7
  Basket 4.1
  Basket Removal 4.7
  Belt 4.1
  Cabinet 4.5
  Clutch 4.1, 4.5
  Console 4.4
  Drain Pump 4.2, 4.3
  Drive Motor 4.1
  Fill Valve 4.4
  Interlocks 4.2
  Leaks 4.2
  Lid Switch 4.2
  Lower Bearing
    Causing Leaks 4.2
    Service / Replacement 4.8
  Pump. *See* General Electric Front Access: Drain Pump
  Suspension 4.2, 4.5
  Switches 4.4
  Timer 4.5
  Transmission 4.1
    Removal 4.7
  Tub Removal 4.6
  Water Level Switch 4.2
General Electric Old-Style Machines
  Agitator 3.6
    "Handwash" 3.6
  Agitator Spline 3.6
  Belt, Drive 3.10
  Cabinet 3.2
  Clutch 3.1, 3.10
  Console 3.2
  Drive Motor 3.1, 3.13
  Friction Pads 3.15
  Leaks 3.3
  Lid Switch 3.9
  Noisy Operation 3.5
  Oil Leaks 3.5
  Pump 3.2, 3.5
  Pump Coupling 3.5
  Relay 3.13
  Snubber Blocks 3.15
  Starting Relay 3.13
  Timer 3.9
  Transmission Removal 3.14
  Tub Boot. *See* General Electric, Old-Style: Tub Seal
  Tub Seal 3.3, 3.7
  Vibration 3.5, 3.15
  Water Level Switch 3.9
Green Wire. *See* **Ground Lead**
Ground Lead 1.5, 2.11

H

Hoses
   Drain 2.7
   Fill 2.4
   Leaks. *See* Leaks

I

Imbalance Switch. *See* **Interlock, Imbalance**
Interlock 2.13
   Imbalance 2.13
   Lid Switch 2.13
   Water Level 2.13

L

Leaks 2.7
   Hose 2.8
   Pump 2.8
   Tub 2.8
   Water Fill Valve 2.8
Lid Switch. *See* **Switch, Lid**
Lock, Lid. *See* **Lid Lock**
Logic Board. *See* **Control Board**

M

Motor
   Direct-Reversing 2.9
   Drive 2.9, 2.17
      Stalled 2.17, 2.18
      Starting Switch. *See* Switch: Starting
Multi-Switch. *See* **Switch: Multi**

N

Nameplate 1.2
Noises 2.17

O

Odor. *See* **Smell**
Overfilling of Tub 2.5
Overflow, Drain 2.7. *See also* **Vacuum Break**

P

Parts, Buying 1.2
Pressure Switch, Water Level.
      See **Water Level Switch**
Pump 2.7
   Leaks 2.8

R

Rinse Cycle. *See* **Cycles**

S

Safety Precautions 1.4
Selector Switch. *See* **Switch: Multi**
Siphoning the Tub 1.5
Softener Dispenser. *See* **Dispenser**
Solenoid
   Clutch. *See* Solenoid: Spin
   Testing 2.13
Solenoid Valve
   Bleach or Softener Dispenser 2.2
   Fill 2.3, 2.4
Speed Selector Switch. *See* **Switch: Multi**
Spin Cycle. *See* **Cycles**
Starting Switch. *See* **Switch: Starting**
Switch
   Multi 2.16
   Speed Selector. *See* Switch: Multi
   Starting 2.18
   Water Level. *See* Water Level Switch
   Water Temperature. *See* Switch: Multi
Switch, Lid 2.13. *See also* **Individual Model**
Switches, Testing 2.13

T

Thermistor 2.3, 2.5
Timer
   Digital 2.14
   Testing 2.14
Tools 1.2
Transmission 2.2, 2.9. *See also* **Belt, Drive:**
   Broken
   Locked 2.10
   Oil Leaks 2.10
   Rebuilding 2.10
Tub
   Draining 1.5
Tub Leaks. *See* **Leaks**

V

Vacuum Break 2.6
Volt-Ohmmeter 1.2
   How to Use 1.6
Voltage, Testing 1.6
VOM. *See* **Volt-Ohmmeter**

W

Wash Cycle. *See* **Cycles**
Water Fill Valve. *See* **Solenoid Valve, Fill**
   Leaks 2.8
Water Level Switch 2.3, 2.5
   Strainer 2.4
   Testing 2.14
Water Temperature Switch. *See* **Switch: Multi**
Wiring Diagram, Reading 2.10

Also Available from EB Marketing Group
Brand-Specific Dryer & Top-Loading Washer Manuals!
for those who want a little LESS...
*Our brand-specific manuals have the same high quality instructions and illustrations
as our all-brand manuals, at a new low price!*

7th Edition
Whirlpool Dryer Repair
ISBN 1-890386-36-7   Part No. EBWD

7th Edition
Whirlpool Washer Repair
ISBN 1-890386-35-9   Part No. EBWW

*Whirlpool-brand manuals include
Kenmore, Kitchenaid, Estate
and Roper Brand Machines*

7th Edition
GE/Hotpoint Dryer Repair
ISBN 1-890386-38-3   Part No. EBGD

7th Edition
GE/Hotpoint Washer Repair
ISBN 1-890386-37-5   Part No. EBGW

*GE-brand manuals include
Hotpoint, late-model RCA, and
JC Penney (Penncrest) Brand Machines*

7th Edition
Maytag Dryer Repair
ISBN 1-890386-40-5   Part No. EBMD

7th Edition
Maytag Washer Repair
ISBN 1-890386-39-1   Part No. EBMW

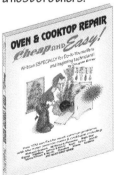